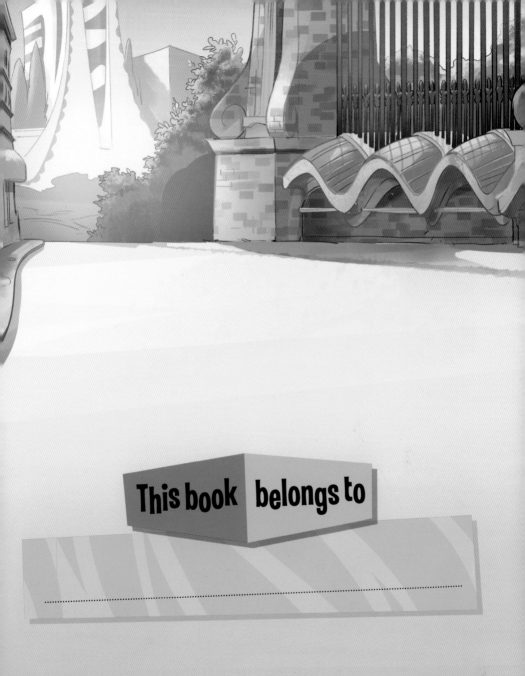

This book belongs to

....

This edition published by Parragon Books Ltd in 2016

Parragon Books Ltd
Chartist House
15–17 Trim Street
Bath BA1 1HA, UK
www.parragon.com

ISBN 978-1-4748-2782-9

Printed in China

Disney
ZOOTROPOLIS
JUDY'S
DREAM FILES

PaRRagon

Bath · New York · Cologne · Melbourne · Delhi
Hong Kong · Shenzhen · Singapore · Amsterdam

Judy Hopps had dreamed of becoming a police officer since she was a little bunny living in Bunnyburrow. She had finished top in her class at the Police Academy, and now she had left her family behind to move to the big city – Zootropolis!

Judy would be the first ever rabbit police officer in the Zootropolis Police Department (ZPD) and she couldn't wait to get started. She was a firm believer in the city's motto: 'Anyone can be anything!'

On her first day at the ZPD, Judy was by far the smallest animal in the room, but she didn't let that bother her. The police chief, Bogo, arrived and began assigning tasks. He handed out 14 missing mammal cases to his officers, finally reaching Judy's name.

"And last," he said, "our token bunny, Officer Hopps."

Judy sat up straight, excited to hear her assignment.

"Parking duty!" Bogo announced. "Dismissed!"

Judy couldn't believe it. She had come to Zootropolis to fight crime, but instead she was going to be a traffic warden!

Even so, Judy was determined to be a *fantastic* traffic warden.
She headed out in her electric cart and handed out 201 tickets by noon!
Just before lunch, she saw an argument in a nearby ice-cream parlour.
The owner, an elephant called Jerry, was refusing to serve a fox and his
son because he thought they would make a mess in his shop.

"I simply want to buy a Jumbo-pop for my little boy," the fox said.
Judy, who was in line behind them, stepped forward to help.

Judy hated to see any animal treated this way, so she showed her ZPD badge and ordered Jerry to serve the fox and his son, who was wearing a cute little elephant costume.

On the pavement outside, the fox turned to Judy.

"Officer," he said. "I really can't thank you enough."

Judy introduced herself, and the fox told her his name.

"Wilde. Nick Wilde."

Then they went their separate ways.

Later that afternoon, Judy spotted Nick and his son again. They were melting down the Jumbo-pop to make hundreds of little pawpsicles, then selling them! Nick was making a lot of money, and the little fox wasn't really his son – he was an adult fox and Nick's partner in crime.

Judy angrily confronted Nick. "You are a liar!" she cried.

"It's called a hustle, sweetheart," Nick calmly replied.

Judy tried to arrest Nick, but he pointed out he hadn't actually done anything illegal. He told Judy she'd never be a real cop.

"Underestimating me, you'll find, is a big mistake," Judy warned him.

"All right, look," said Nick, "everyone comes to Zootropolis thinking they can be anything they want. Well, you can't. You can only be what you are." He pointed to himself and said, "Sly fox." Then he pointed to Judy and said, "Dumb bunny."

"I am NOT a dumb bunny!" Judy cried.

"Yeah and that's not wet cement," Nick replied.

Judy looked down. She had walked right into wet cement and now she was stuck! Nick walked off and Judy could only watch him go.

The next day, Judy found it hard to keep smiling as she worked.
She kept telling herself she WAS a real cop, but she wasn't too sure.

Suddenly, a pig started banging on the window of her cart.
He'd been robbed! Judy jumped out and chased the thief, a weasel,
across town and into Little Rodentia, a tiny burrough where
rodents lived. The weasel was clever and quick, but Officer Hopps
finally managed to catch him.

Back at the ZPD, Chief Bogo was angry with Judy for abandoning her traffic-warden duties. As he was talking, an otter stormed in.

"My husband has been missing for 10 days!" the otter exclaimed.

"Mrs Otterton, our detectives are very busy," sighed Chief Bogo. Judy saw her chance. "I will find him!" she proclaimed.

Before Chief Bogo could turn Judy down, Assistant Mayor Bellwether arrived. "I just heard Officer Hopps is taking the case!"

Bellwether was so pleased that a rabbit was being given a chance as a police officer, Chief Bogo couldn't argue. But he gave Judy just two days to solve the case, and if she failed, she had to leave the ZPD.

In the missing-mammal file, Judy saw a photograph of Mrs Otterton's husband, Emmitt, holding one of Nick Wilde's pawpsicles. Maybe Nick knew where Emmitt was!

Judy tracked Nick down. Using a hidden microphone in her carrot-shaped pen, she recorded Nick admitting that he didn't pay tax. She promised to keep it secret if Nick agreed to help her.

Nick took Judy to the last place he had seen Emmitt – a health spa. There they met a yak called Yax, who remembered the licence plate of the car Emmitt had left in.

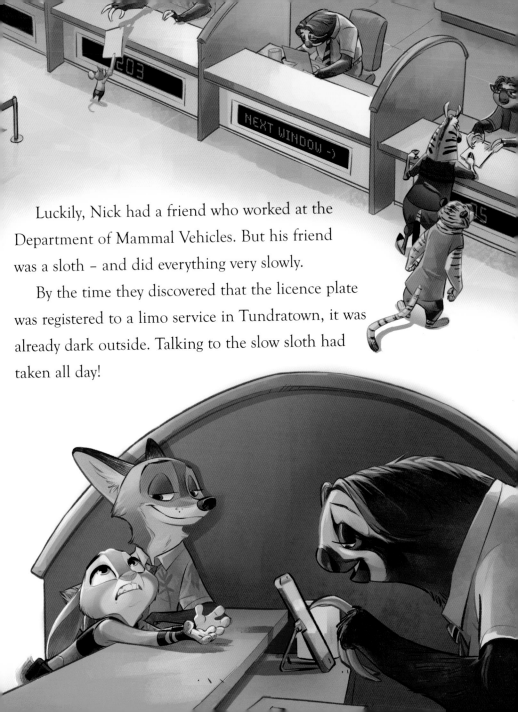

Luckily, Nick had a friend who worked at the Department of Mammal Vehicles. But his friend was a sloth – and did everything very slowly.

By the time they discovered that the licence plate was registered to a limo service in Tundratown, it was already dark outside. Talking to the slow sloth had taken all day!

When Judy and Nick tracked down the limo, they found Emmitt's wallet lying on the floor and the car seats covered in claw marks. The driver of the limo, a jaguar called Manchas, told them that Emmitt had gone crazy.

"He was an *animal*, down on all fours ... he was a savage," Manchas told them. "Just kept yelling 'night howlers' over and over."

Then Manchas suddenly stopped being friendly. He got on to all fours and started chasing Judy and Nick! Eventually Judy managed to trap Manchas and call for police back-up.

But by the time Chief Bogo and his officers arrived, Manchas had disappeared! Nick and Judy were sure someone must have helped him escape when they weren't looking.

Chief Bogo didn't believe the story. He demanded that Judy hand over her badge and resign immediately.

Nick spoke up. "You gave her 48 hours," he told the chief, "so technically we still have 10 left to find our Mr Otterton, and that's exactly what we are gonna do."

With that, Nick pulled Judy away, leaving Chief Bogo stunned.

Nick had an idea – whoever had helped Manchas escape would have been caught on the city's traffic cameras. He and Judy accessed the footage and saw a group of wolves bundle Manchas into a van, which then sped off to a huge building on the edge of town. These wolves must be the 'night howlers' that Emmitt had raved about!

Nick and Judy raced to the building and sneaked inside. Judy shone her torch around. There were 15 animals locked in cages, including Emmitt and Manchas. The animals were standing on all fours and growling – they had gone savage!

"All the missing mammals are right here," Judy said.

Suddenly, Judy and Nick heard a noise at the door. They hid in the shadows as someone walked in, shouting. "Enough! I don't want excuses, Doctor, I want answers!"

It was Lionheart, the mayor of Zootropolis! Judy started recording Lionheart and the doctor on her phone.

"Something has awakened their savage instincts," the doctor said.

Just then, Judy's phone started beeping. Before Lionheart could spot them, Judy and Nick ran.

Back at the ZPD, Judy played her recording to Chief Bogo. He was shocked! He had Mayor Lionheart arrested for caging the animals, then ordered tests to find out why they had turned savage. Assistant Mayor Bellwether would now be mayor of Zootropolis.

Later, while Judy waited to speak to the press, she gave Nick her carrot pen with the recording of him. She trusted him now – he had kept his side of the deal and helped her to find Mr Otterton.

But during the press conference, Judy let it slip that only predator animals were turning savage. As a predator himself, Nick was upset as he knew this was going to cause trouble between predators and prey in Zootropolis. He left feeling angry.

As Nick predicted, Judy had caused chaos in the city. The animals started fighting and nobody trusted predators anymore. Despite this, Bellwether asked Judy to become the new face of the ZPD.

Judy was shocked. She didn't feel like a hero – she felt like she had broken the city. She quit the police force and returned to her family farm, feeling like a failure. But one day soon after, she heard someone at her father's farm yell at a bunny to avoid the 'night howlers' because their pollen had a strange effect on animals. Judy suddenly realized that night howlers were flowers....

"The flowers are making the predators go savage," Judy said to herself. "That's it! That's what I've been missing!"

Judy jumped straight into the family truck and drove back to the city. She found Nick and apologized.

"I've been fighting my whole life to break out of my box and to be all I can be," she said. "Then what do I do? I put my friend and partner in a box."

Nick turned round and smiled – he had recorded Judy's apology on her carrot pen! He forgave her and the two friends climbed into the truck. They had to find out who was using the night howlers! As they drove off, Nick ate a handful of blueberries from a crate on the front seat.

Judy and Nick got on the trail of the night howlers and discovered an old train carriage full of them. A sheep was turning the plants' pollen into blue pellets and loading them into a dart gun!

In that moment, Judy and Nick realized that Bellwether was behind the scheme! She wanted to make the animals in the city scared of each other, so she could have power over everyone.

Judy and Nick managed to grab a case with a dart gun inside. They stole the train carriage and headed back towards the ZPD, taking a shortcut through the empty National History Museum.

But Bellwether was at the museum! Two huge rams blocked Nick and Judy's path and grabbed the case from them. The rams pushed the pair into a pit in the floor – they were trapped.

Bellwether took the dart gun out of the case and fired a pellet at Nick! Then she phoned the police to report a savage animal.

Nick hunched over and snarled at Judy, ready to strike ...

... but then Nick stopped and smiled.

"What you've got in that weapon, those are blueberries," he said.

Nick had replaced the night-howler pellets with blueberries!

Then he held up the carrot pen: he had recorded the whole thing.

Just then, the ZPD arrived and arrested Bellwether.

Once Bellwether was gone, Zootropolis quickly returned to normal. The savage mammals were cured, Mrs Otterton got her husband back, Lionheart was released ... and Nick joined the ZPD!

"Still believe it?" Nick asked Judy as they sat in their patrol car.

"That anyone can be anything?" Judy replied. "Mmm, yeah, I do. Even if it's not quite as simple as all that. But the thing is, we'll never know what we can be or what's possible if we don't try."

Suddenly a red sports car sped past them. Nick switched on the siren and Judy put her foot down. It was time to fight some crime!

The End

Who's who?

Are you ready to meet some of the creatures living and working in Zootropolis? Find out who they are and what they do!

Name: Judy Hopps
Species: Rabbit
Prey or Predator: Prey
Job: Police officer, traffic warden

Name: Leodore Lionheart
Species: Lion
Prey or Predator: Predator
Job: Mayor of Zootropolis

Name: Bellwether
Species: Sheep
Prey or Predator: Prey
Job: Assistant Mayor of Zootropolis

Name: Bogo
Species: Cape buffalo
Prey or Predator: Predator
Job: Chief of Police

Name: Clawhauser
Species: Cheetah
Prey or Predator: Predator
Job: Police officer, front desk

Name: Nick Wilde
Species: Fox
Prey or Predator: Predator
Job: Hustler

Name: Finnick
Species: Fennec fox
Prey or Predator: Predator
Job: Hustler

Now you've met the most important creatures in Zootropolis, it's time to tell them all about you! Fill in this fact file.

All about YOU!

STICK IN A PHOTO OR DRAW A PICTURE OF YOURSELF HERE!

Name: ....

Nickname: ....

Birthday: ....

Hair colour: ....

Eye colour: ....

Best friend: ....

Pets: ....

....

Top talent: ....

Worst habit: ....

Likes: ....

....

Dislikes: ....

....

Animal antics

Imagine you are an animal living in Zootropolis ... What animal would you be? Circle your top choice from the creatures below, or write an alternative option!

BEAR Buffalo

Squirrel LION Rabbit

ELEPHANT PANTHER

Mouse FOX

WOLF Sheep

Cheetah RHINO

Shrew

HIPPO Deer

I would be a ....

DRAW A PICTURE OF YOU AS AN ANIMAL!

Mammal metropolis

There are lots of different neighbourhoods in the bustling city of Zootropolis, from Tundratown and Little Rodentia to the Rainforest District. What's it like where you live?

Write the name of the place where you live:

I live in ....

Is it a:

◯ **Town**

◯ **Village**

◯ **City**

Have you always lived there?

◯ **Yes**   ◯ **No**

Tick the words that best describe where you live:

◯ **Busy**   ◯ **Peaceful**

◯ **Loud**   ◯ **Friendly**

◯ **Quiet**   ◯ **Beautiful**

Where would you like to live in Zootropolis?

- ○ **Bunnyburrow**
- ○ **Tundratown**
- ○ **The Rainforest District**
- ○ **Savannah Central**
- ○ **The Meadowlands**
- ○ **Little Rodentia**

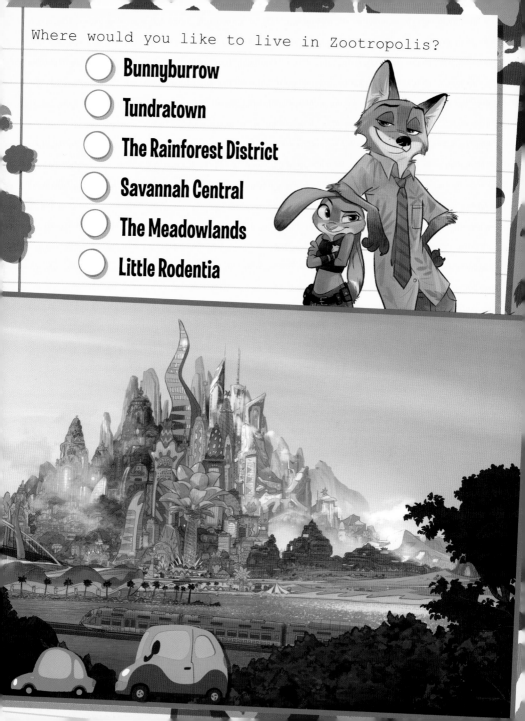

Home sweet home!

When Judy Hopps moves out of her family home in Bunnyburrow, she lives in an apartment in downtown Zootropolis. She has two ve noisy neighbours, Kudu and Oryx! Tell Judy all about your home...

Do you have neighbours?

☐ **Yes**   ☐ **No**

Do you have your own room or do you share?

☐ **Own room**   ☐ **Shared room**

Describe your home:

....

....

....

Describe your bedroom:

....

....

....

What's your favourite part of your home?

....

....

Family files

Judy has a large family, with lots of bunny cousins! She misses them when she moves away from Bunnyburrow, but they keep in touch via video chat. Judy would love to learn a bit about your family....

Mum's name: ....

Dad's name: ....

Brothers' names: ....

Sisters' names: ....

STICK IN A PHOTO OF YOUR FAMILY.

Who makes you laugh the most?

....

Who is the best at helping out?

....

Who is the noisiest?

....

Who gives the best hugs?

....

Tick the words you think best describe your family:

○ **Large**　　○ **Happy**

○ **Noisy**　　○ **Small**

○ **Fun**　　　○ **Talented**

○ **Clever**　　○ **Helpful**

JUDY'S PARENTS, STU AND BONNIE, ARE SO PROUD OF HER.

Dream BIG!

Judy dreams of being a cop, keeping creatures safe and making Zootropolis a better place. What are your biggest dreams? Tick your answers in the lists below.

My dream job:
- ⭐ **Astronaut**
- ⭐ **Police officer**
- ⭐ **Pirate**
- ⭐ **Artist**
- ⭐ **Explorer**
- ⭐ **Dancer**

My dream holiday:
- ⭐ **Beach**
- ⭐ **Rainforest**
- ⭐ **Desert**
- ⭐ **Mountain**
- ⭐ **Jungle**
- ⭐ **City**

My dream animal:
- ⭐ **Lion**
- ⭐ **Squirrel**
- ⭐ **Monkey**
- ⭐ **Polar bear**
- ⭐ **Giraffe**
- ⭐ **Rabbit**

My dream home:
- ⭐ **Castle**
- ⭐ **Igloo**
- ⭐ **Submarine**
- ⭐ **Tepee**
- ⭐ **Mansion**
- ⭐ **Cave**

THE ZOOTROPOLIS MOTTO:
'Anyone can be anything!'

WRITE ABOUT YOUR DREAMS FOR THE FUTURE!

Judy and Nick are very different creatures, but that doesn't stop them becoming the best of friends. Fill in everything you know about your best friends!

Friends fur-ever!

Friend 1

Name: ....

Birthday: ....

What I like best about them:

....

Something we have in common:

....

Something that makes us different:

....

Stick in a picture!

Friend 2

Name: ....

Birthday: ....

What I like best about them:

....

Something we have in common:

....

Something that makes us different:

....

Stick in a picture!

Friend 3

Name: ....

Birthday: ....

What I like best about them:

....

Something we have in common:

....

Something that makes us different:

....

Stick in a picture!

Friend 4

Name: ....

Birthday: ....

What I like best about them:

....

Something we have in common:

....

Something that makes us different:

....

Stick in a picture!

Friend 5

Name: ....

Birthday: ....

What I like best about them:

....

Something we have in common:

....

Something that makes us different:

....

Stick in a picture!

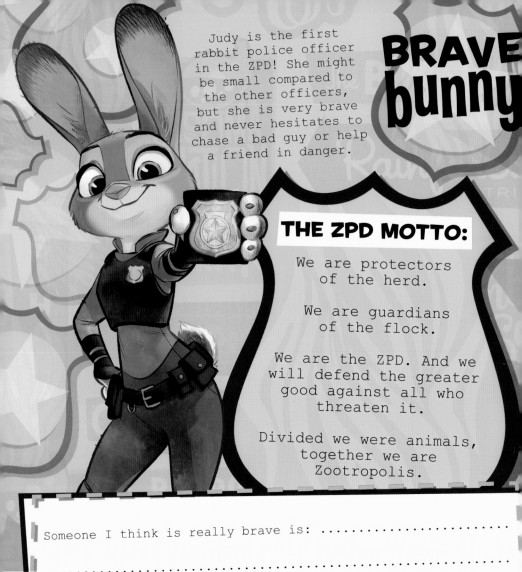

Judy is the first rabbit police officer in the ZPD! She might be small compared to the other officers, but she is very brave and never hesitates to chase a bad guy or help a friend in danger.

BRAVE bunny

THE ZPD MOTTO:

We are protectors of the herd.

We are guardians of the flock.

We are the ZPD. And we will defend the greater good against all who threaten it.

Divided we were animals, together we are Zootropolis.

Someone I think is really brave is: ....

....

I think they're brave because: ....

....

Think of a time when you were brave and write all about it here. Then the next time you feel scared, you can look back at what you've written and remember how brave you really are!

A time when I was really brave was:

. . . .

. . . .

. . . .

. . . .

. . . .

. . . .

. . . .

. . . .

. . . .

. . . .

. . . .

. . . .

. . . .

. . . .

Dream team

Judy loves being a cop and feeling like she's part of a team. It's even better when Nick joins the ZPD and she has a partner! Imagine your dream team.... You could play a sport, dance on stage, be superheroes or even fight crime!

What would your team be called?

Team ....

How many members would it have? ....

Who would be part of your team?

Write their names here and give each of them a special team nickname!

TEAM MEMBER 1

Name: ....

Nickname: ....

TEAM MEMBER 2

Name: ....

Nickname: ....

TEAM MEMBER 3

Name: ....

Nickname: ....

TEAM MEMBER 4

Name: ....

Nickname: ....

DESIGN AND COLOUR A COOL UNIFORM FOR YOUR TEAM HERE!

Nick is wily and cunning. Judy is brave and kind. Look at all the words listed below and choose the best one to describe each of your friends!

Which word?

CLEVER

Happy

Brave

Funny

SHY

KIND

Serious

Musical

COOL

Stylish

Imaginative

CONFIDENT

Silly

Caring

GENEROUS

Friend 1

Name: ....

Word: ....

Friend 2

Name: ....

Word: ....

Friend 3

Name: ....

Word: ....

Friend 4

Name: ....

Word: ....

Friend 5

Name: ....

Word: ....

What word would your friends pick to describe you?

Word: ....

Opposites attract!

Nick and Judy are opposites in lots of ways, but despite their differences they become friends and they stick together through thick and thin.

Judy

FEMALE

LITTLE

PREY

COP

GOOD

Nick

MALE

BIG

PREDATOR

HUSTLER

NAUGHTY

Hot Cold

Circle which you prefer from these pairs of opposites.

Sweet Sour

Summer Winter

Tall Short

Indoors Outdoors

Wet Dry

Sunny Cloudy

Smooth Rough

Light Dark

Early Late

Day Night

Predator Prey

Hard Soft

Full Empty

Loud Quiet

Black White

A helping hand

Together Nick and Judy are a dynamic crime-fighting, mystery-solving duo. They are always there to help each other out! Which of your friends or family would you choose to help you in the following situations?

You can't answer a question in your homework.

I would ask .... for help.

You've forgotten the lyrics to a song.

I would ask .... for help.

You need to pick an outfit for a special event.

I would ask .... for help.

You want to create a new dance routine.

I would ask .... for help.

You're stuck on a level of a computer game.

I would ask .... for help.

You need to plan a surprise party.

I would ask .... for help.

Nick helped Judy to solve a huge crime
and save Zootropolis! Write about a time
when a friend helped you to solve a problem.

. . . .

. . . .

. . . .

. . . .

. . . .

. . . .

. . . .

. . . .

. . . .

. . . .

. . . .

. . . .